Celebration Series®

Piano Repertoire 2

2015 Edition

FREDERICK
HARRIS
MUSIC

Celebration Series®, 2015 Edition

The Royal Conservatory is pleased to present the fifth edition of *Celebration Series®*. The *Celebration Series®* was first published in 1987 to international acclaim. This edition of the series includes twelve books of repertoire (Preparatory A–Level 10), and ten books of etudes (Levels 1–10), providing students with a wealth of outstanding repertoire to explore.

The repertoire comprises a carefully selected grouping of pieces from the Baroque, Classical, Romantic, and contemporary style periods. The Preparatory A and Preparatory B repertoire books include a variety of creative teaching pieces to inspire students in their first and second year of study. The repertoire in Levels 1–10 is divided into "lists" according to style period. Within each list you will discover a rich selection of pieces that will appeal to a variety of musical tastes and abilities.

The etudes books present compositions especially suited for building the technique and artistry to support pianistic development at each level. A brief description of the technical focus of each etude is included in the table of contents for Levels 1–8.

With this edition, we are pleased to include a recording for each piece in the series. These outstanding recordings by concert artists may be used by students as a reliable resource for style-period performance practice. The recordings can be accessed online at www.rcmusic.ca/digital-learning with the code printed in the back of each book.

Celebration Series®, 2015 Edition is sure to inspire students as they continue on their musical journey.

A Note on Editing and Performance Practice

Most Baroque and early Classical composers wrote few dynamics, articulation, or other performance indications in their scores. Interpretation was left up to the performer, with the expectation that the performance practice was understood. Even into the 19th century, composers' scores could vary from copy to copy or edition to edition. The editors of *Celebration Series®* have consulted original sources wherever possible and have kept editorial additions to a minimum.

Metronome markings include a range to assist the student and teacher in arriving at a suitable tempo for each piece. Editorial markings, including fingering and the execution of ornaments, are intended to be helpful rather than definitive.

This edition follows the policy that the bar line cancels accidentals. In accordance with the current practice, cautionary accidentals are added only in cases of possible ambiguity.

For examination requirements of The Royal Conservatory Certificate Program, please refer to the *Piano Syllabus, 2015 Edition*.

Elaine Rusk

Vice President, The Royal Conservatory Certificate Program

Contents

Allegretto in C Major

Christian Gottlob Neefe
(1748–1798)

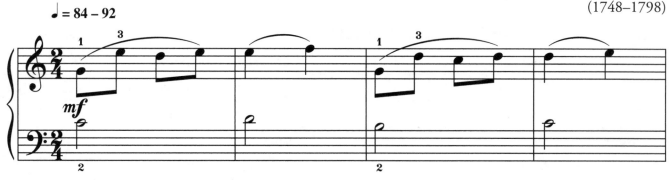

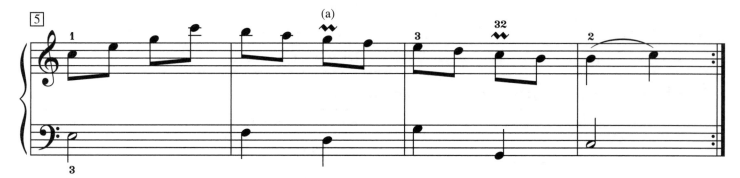

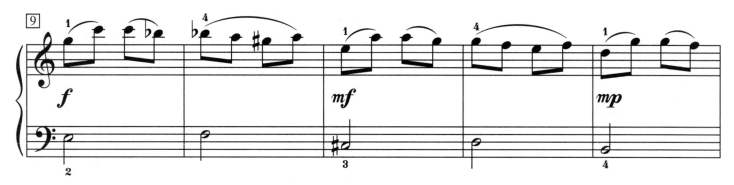

For examinations, the ornaments are optional.

Impertinence

HWV 494

George Frideric Handel
(1685–1759)

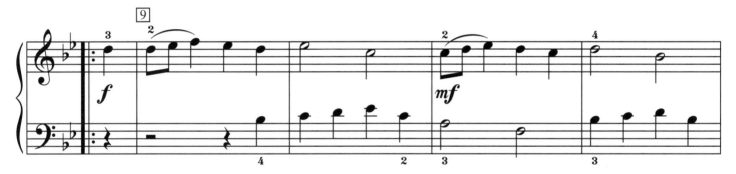

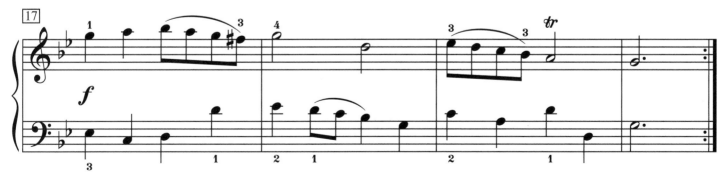

For examinations, the ornaments are optional.

Menuet en rondeau

Minuet in Rondo Form

Jean-Philippe Rameau
(1683–1764)

Left-hand quarter notes may be played detached.
For examinations, the ornaments are optional:

Rameau's original left-hand part contains sustained notes in mm. 7, 8, and 15.
Source: *Pièces de clavecin* (1724)

Gavotte in A Major

Daniel Gottlob Türk
(1750–1813)

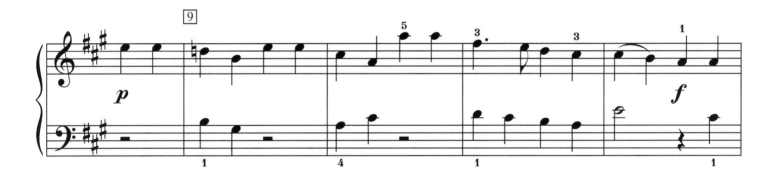

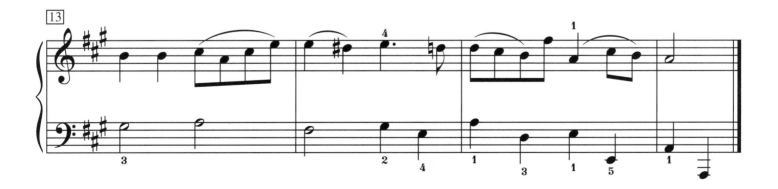

Source: *Handstücke für angehende Klavierspieler,* book 2

Menuetto in C Major

Wolfgang Amadeus Mozart
(1756–1791)

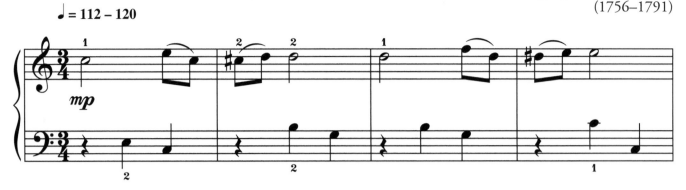

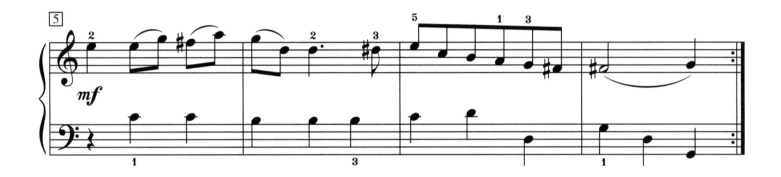

Left-hand notes may be played detached.
Source: First minuet of the third movement of Sonata in C Major for Keyboard or Keyboard and Violin, K 6.

Air in D Minor

ZT 676

Henry Purcell
(1659–1695)

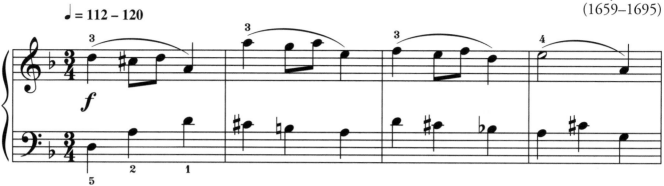

German Dance in B flat Major

Hob. IX:22, no. 5

Franz Joseph Haydn
(1732–1809)

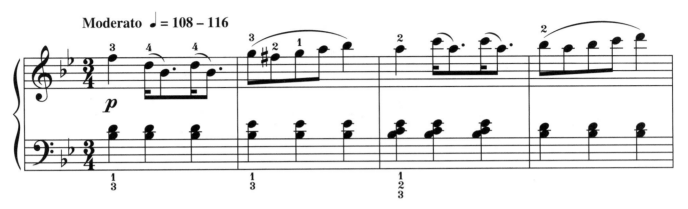

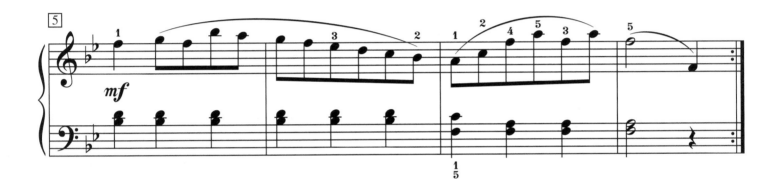

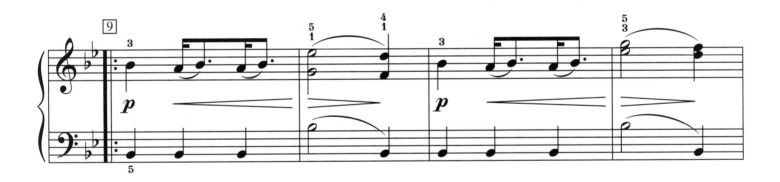

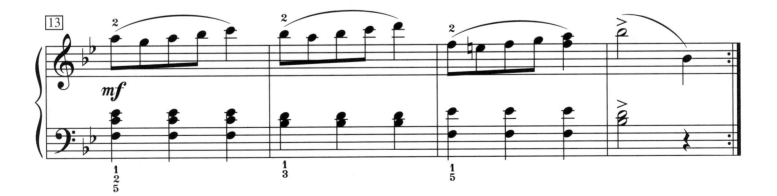

Source: *Ballo Tedescho per il cembalo,* Hob. IX:22

Écossaise in G Major

WoO 23

Ludwig van Beethoven
(1770–1827)

Allegro ♩ = 96 – 104

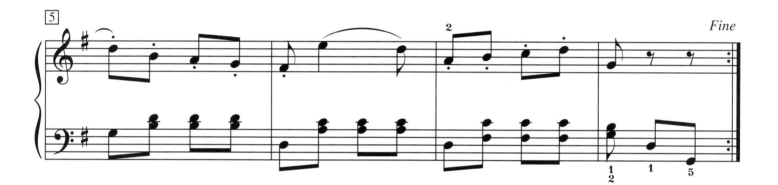

For examinations, the notes in brackets may be omitted.
Original title: *Écossaise für Militarmusik* (1810)
Source: Only this arrangement remains of the original work, initially composed for wind band.

Soldier's March

op. 68, no. 2

Robert Schumann
(1810–1856)

Munter und straff * ♩ = 116 – 126

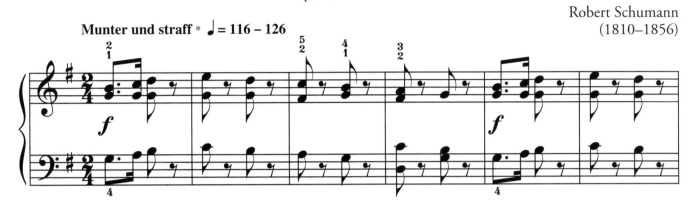

*vigorous and strict
Source: *Album für die Jugend,* op. 68

On a Quiet Lake

William Gillock
(1917–1993)

Slowly drifting along ♩ = 84 – 92

Source: *Accent on Majors*

Fanfare

op. 60, no. 8

Vincent Persichetti
(1915–1987)

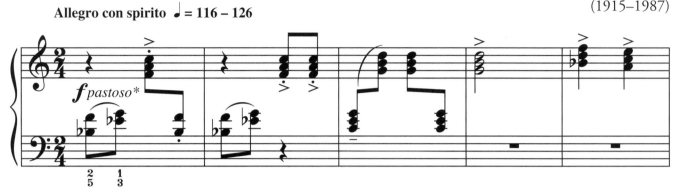

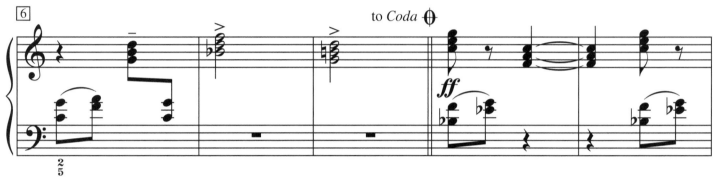

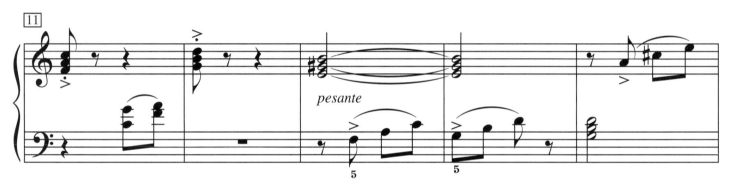

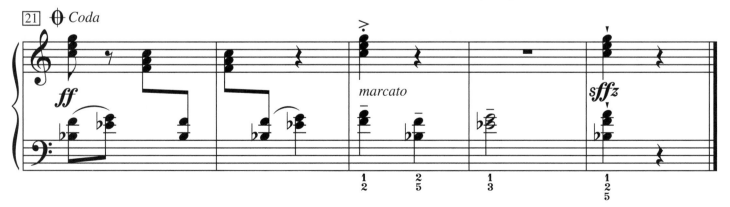

* mellow

Source: *Little Piano Book,* op. 60

A Little Song

op. 27, no. 2

Dmitri Kabalevsky
(1904–1987)

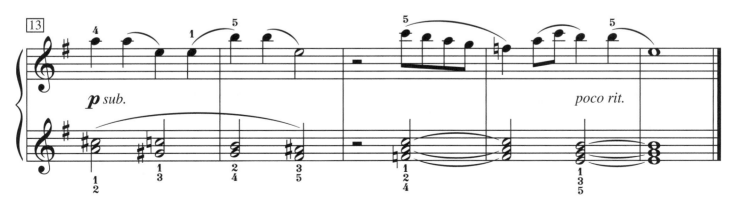

Source: *Thirty Children's Pieces,* op. 27

Atacama Desert

Wynn-Anne Rossi
(b. 1956)

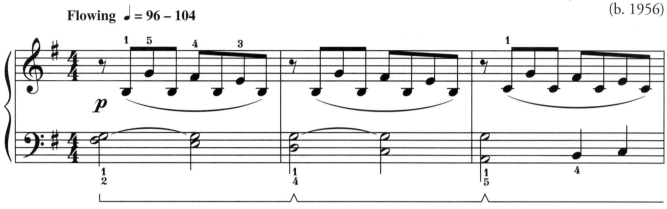

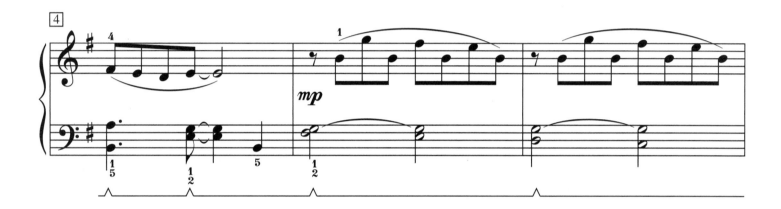

Original title: *Desierto de Atacama*
Source: *Música Latina*, book 2

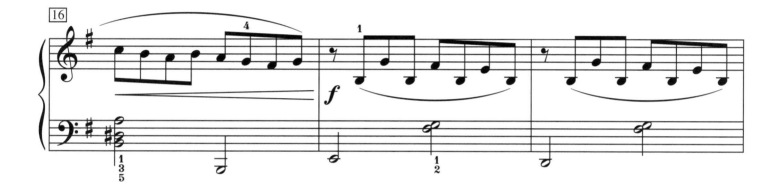

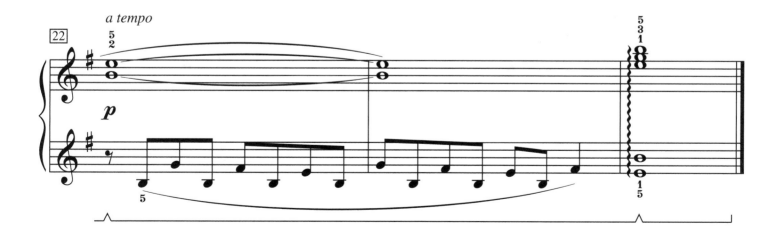

Half Asleep

Christopher Norton
(b. 1953)

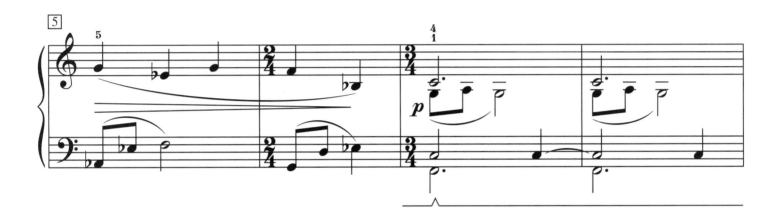

Source: *Christopher Norton Connections® for Piano* 2. To access a complete listing of audio tracks for this collection, visit www.christophernortonconnections.com and enter access code **wzpxn8pe.**

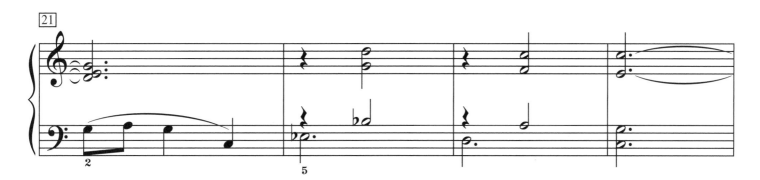

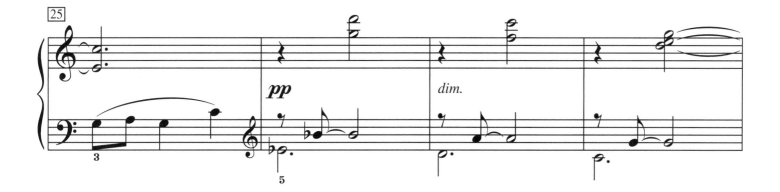

Prelude

Octavio Pinto
(1890–1950)

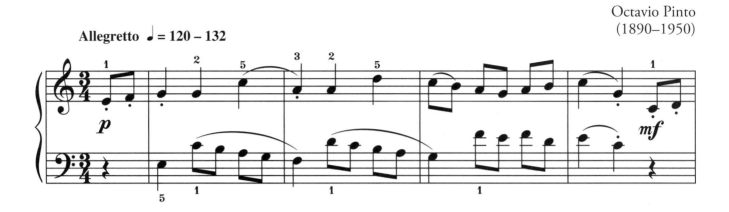

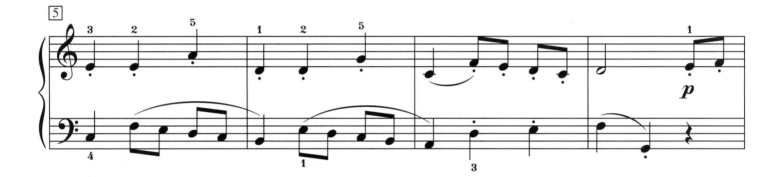

Source: *Children's Festival (Festa de Crianças)*

Little Red Wagon

Teresa Richert
(b. 1964)

Playfully ♩ = 138 – 152

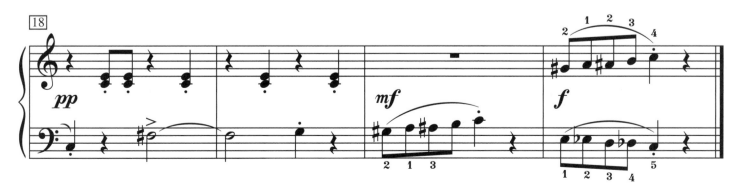

Source: *Toy Collection*

Quiet Lagoon

Jon George
(1944–1982)

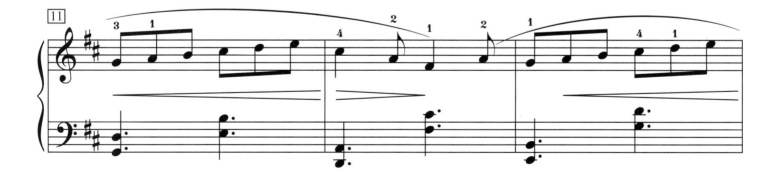

Source: *The Music Tree: Students' Choice,* part 4

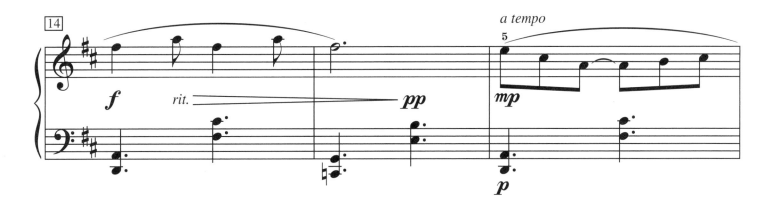

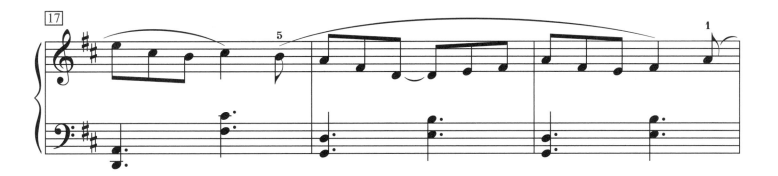

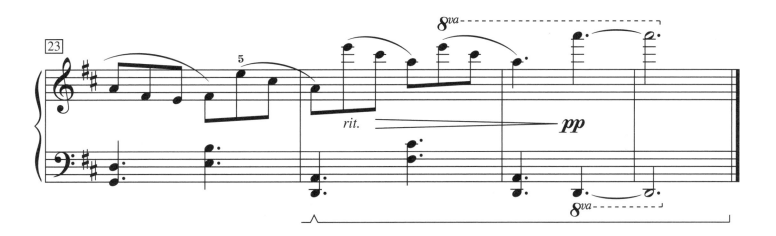

The Silent Moon

Nancy Telfer
(b. 1950)

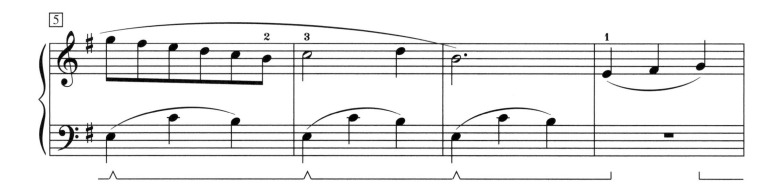

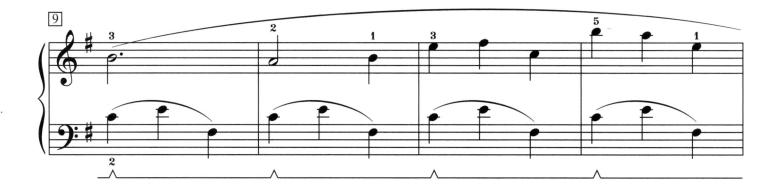

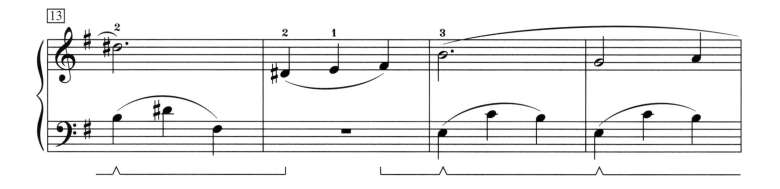

Source: *The Sun and the Moon*

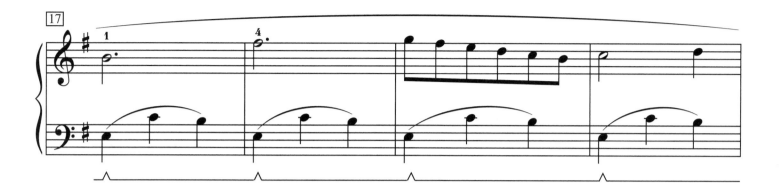

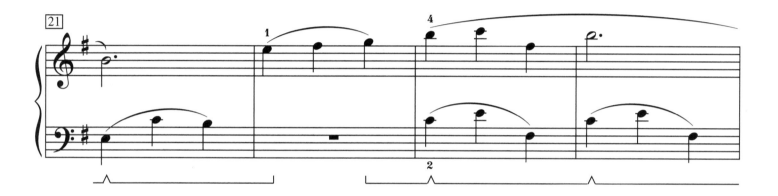

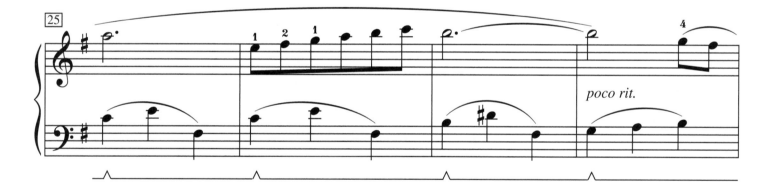

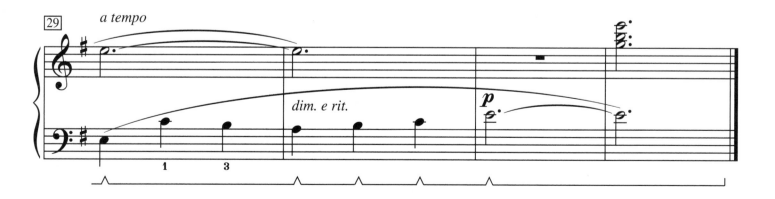

Little Piece No. 3

Marko Tajčević
(1900–1984)

Allegretto scherzando ♩ = 92 – 100

For examinations, the notes in brackets may be omitted.
Source: *Songs from Mur Island,* no. 3
© Copyright 1992 G. Henle Verlag, München. Printed by permission.

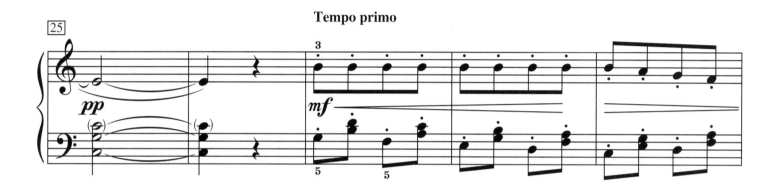

I Spy

Melody Bober
(b. 1955)

March-like ♩ = 152 – 160

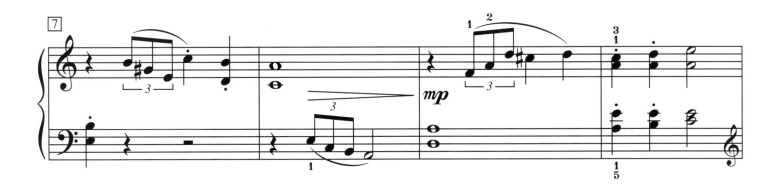

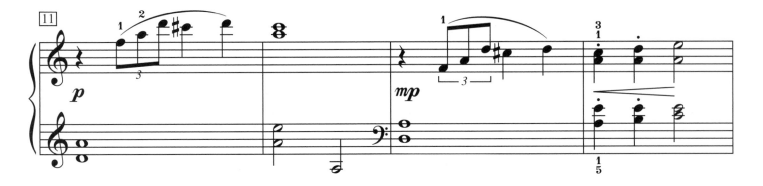

Source: *Grand Solos for Piano,* book 4

Turkish Bazaar

Mark Mrozinski
(b. 1964)

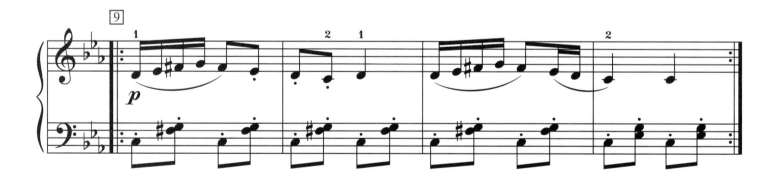

For examinations, observe the repeats.

Source: *Celebrate Piano!*® *Lesson and Musicianship* 4

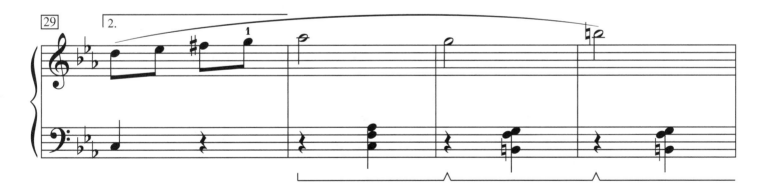

The Sparkling Brook

Margaret Goldston
(1932–2003)

Rushing and melodious ♩ = 132 – 144

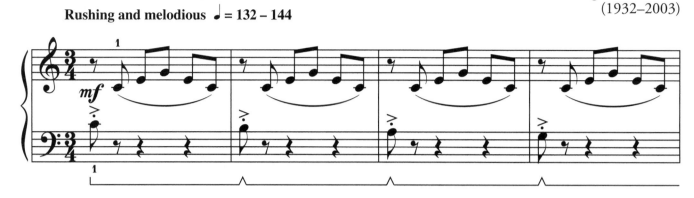

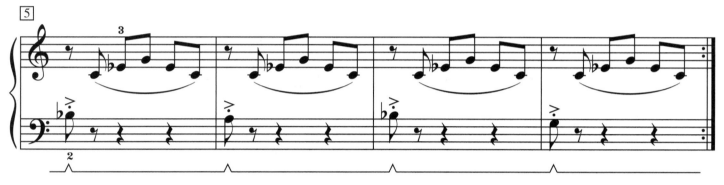

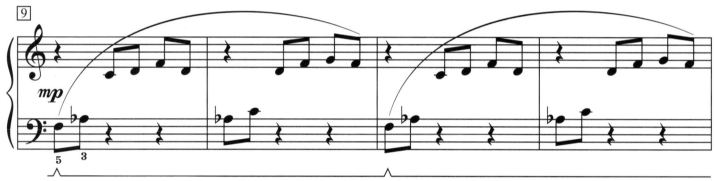

Source: *The Virtuosic Performer*, book 1

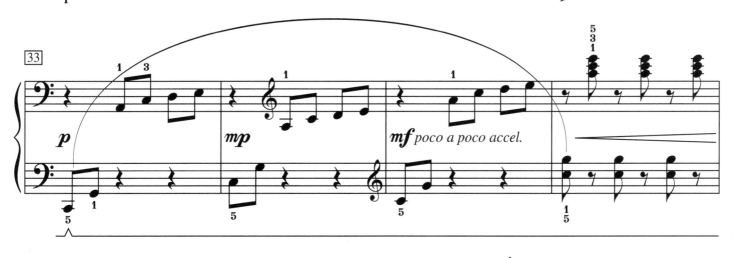

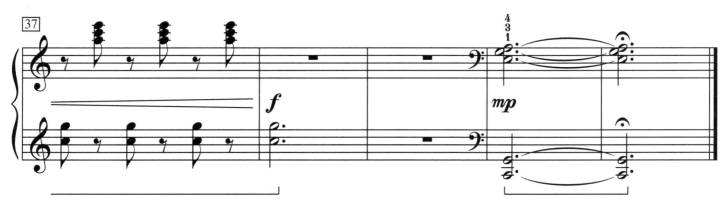

Periwinkle Twinkle

Anne Crosby Gaudet
(b. 1968)

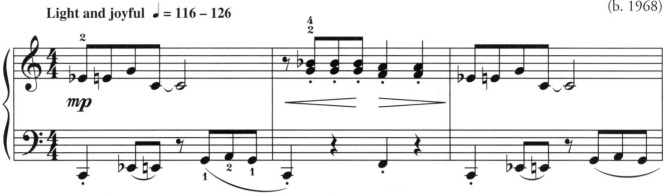

Source: *Tunes in Bloom*

The Waltz That Floated Away

David L. McIntyre
(b. 1950)

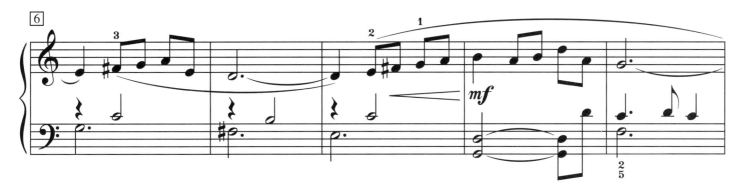

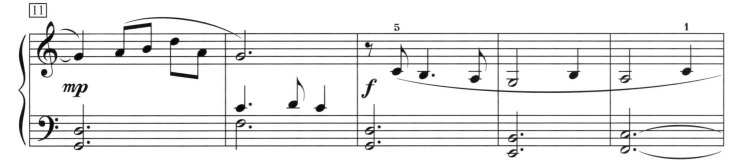

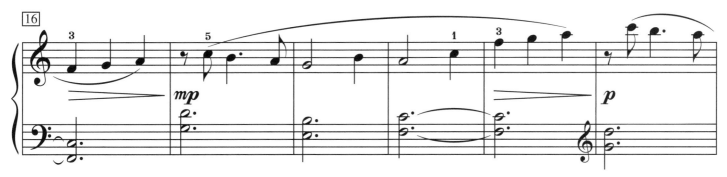

Source: *Pip Squeaks: Four Solos for Young Pianists*

Invention in C Major

Renée Christopher
(b. 1955)

Invention no. 2

Invention in A Minor

Frederick Silvester
(1901–1966)

Invention no. 3

Canon

Cornelius Gurlitt
(1820–1901)

Allegretto ♩ = 112 – 120

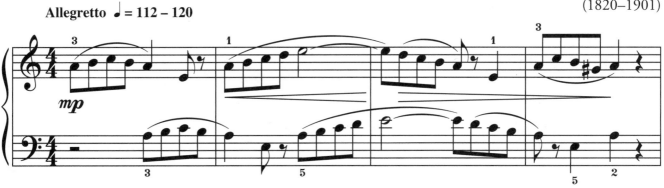

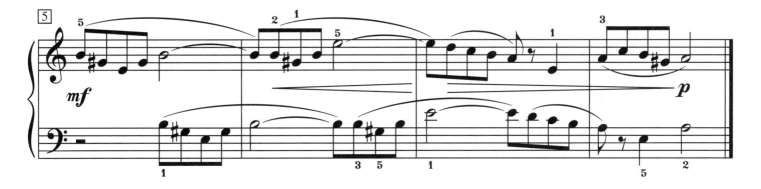

Invention no. 4

Jazz Invention No. 2

Pierre Gallant
(b. 1950)

♩ = 92 – 100

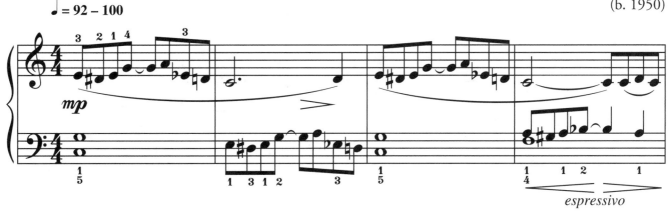

Courageous Cat

Teresa Richert
(b. 1964)

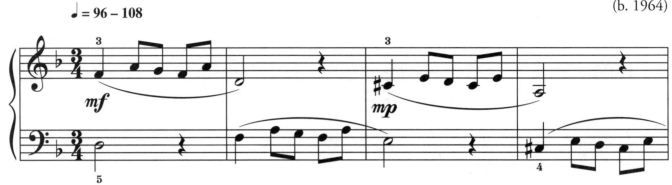

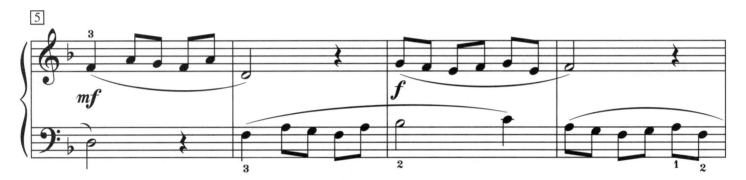

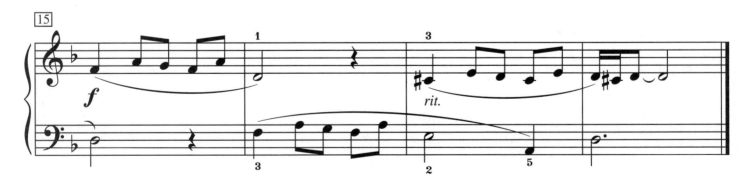

Invention no. 6

Canon in F Major

op. 14, no. 95

Konrad Max Kunz
(1812–1875)

Moderato ♩ = 88 – 96

Source: *200 Short Canons,* op. 14

Little Dance in Canon Form

Béla Bartók
(1881–1945)

Allegro ♩ = 152 – 168

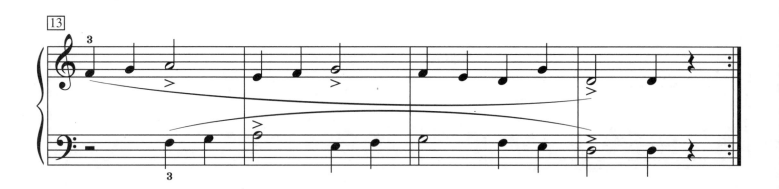